Math **Diagnosis** and **Intervention** System

Teacher's Guide Part 1

Grades K–3: Booklets A–E

Scott Foresman·Addison Wesley

enVisionMATH™

ISBN-13: 978-0-328-31130-9
ISBN-10: 0-328-31130-8

6 7 8 9 10 V084 12 11 10 09

enVisionMATH is trademarked in the U.S. and/or foreign countries of Pearson Education, Inc. or its affiliate(s).

Scott Foresman
is an imprint of

PEARSON

Editorial Offices: Glenview, Illinois • Parsippany, New Jersey • New York, New York
Sales Offices: Boston, Massachusetts • Duluth, Georgia • Glenview, Illinois
Coppell, Texas • Sacramento, California • Chandler, Arizona

Contents

Overview of the Math Diagnosis and Intervention System

1. Assessment

Entry-level assessment
For a student entering Grade 3, assess prerequisite knowledge of Grade 2 content by using the Grade 2 Diagnostic Test, Form A. Or give the Grade 3 Diagnostic Test, Form A, as a pretest on Grade 3 content.

Summative evaluation
Use Form B of a Diagnostic Test to check performance after providing instruction or intervention.

Math Diagnosis and Intervention System
Grade 2 **Diagnostic Test, Form A**

Math Diagnosis and Intervention System
Grade 2 **Diagnostic Test, Form B**

Diagnostic Tests, Forms A and B
Grade-specific, comprehensive

4. Monitoring

Recording progress
On the Individual Record Form, mark test items missed and intervention material assigned.

Informing parents Use at parent conferences. Involve parents in monitoring intervention assignments.

Math Diagnosis and Intervention System
Grade 2 **Individual Record Form**

nd Diagnosis			Intervention
missed nostic B __	OK score (66% or greater)	Actual score. Circle if not OK.	Circle (○) Intervention Lessons assigned.
			A17 A19 A24 A27 A28 A30
			A35 A38 A39 A40
	?/18	___/18	A57 A60 A6?

Individual Record Form
Item analysis and record of intervention assignments

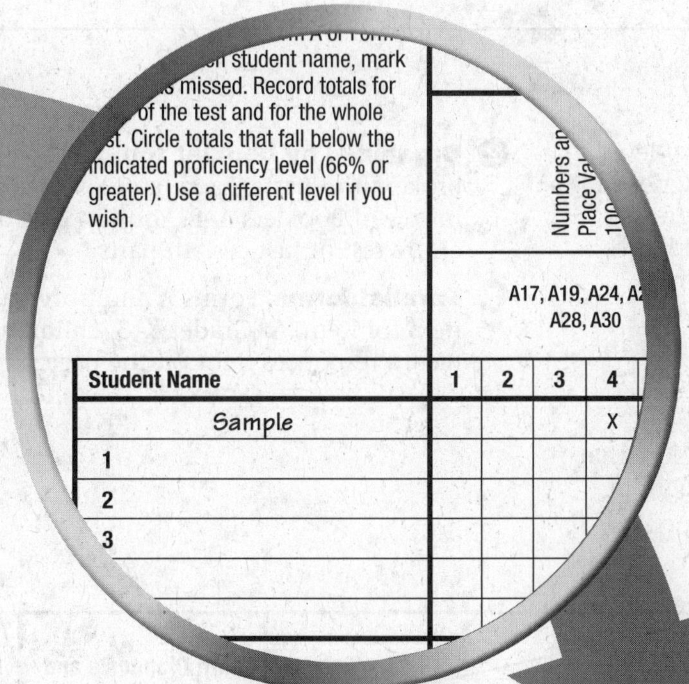

2. Diagnosis

Analysis of Test Results On the Class Record Form, mark test items missed and record scores. If performance is unacceptable, give the Diagnostic Test for the previous grade to determine the student's proficiency level.

Placement Use test results, along with other performance indicators, to make placement decisions. For example, decide whether the student should use the Grade 3 text, the Grade 2 text, or transitional materials such as those found in the Math Diagnosis and Intervention System.

Class Record Form
Item analysis, whole class at a glance

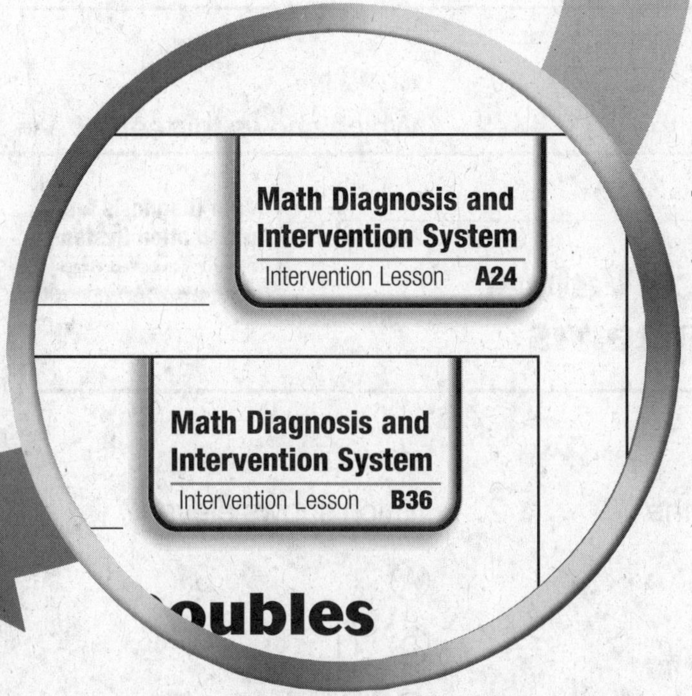

(partial text visible in magnified form:)
...n A or Form...
...en student name, mark
...s missed. Record totals for
... of the test and for the whole
...t. Circle totals that fall below the
...ndicated proficiency level (66% or
greater). Use a different level if you
wish.

Numbers an...
Place Va...
100...

A17, A19, A24, A2...
A28, A30

Student Name	1	2	3	4
Sample				X
1				
2				
3				

3. Intervention

During School Use grade-specific Intervention Lessons for intervention on prerequisite skills at the start of the year, topic, or lesson. Or use for intervention on content taught during the year.

In after-school, Saturday-school, or summer-school (intersession) programs Use as a resource for individualized prescriptions.

Math Diagnosis and Intervention System
Intervention Lesson **A24**

Math Diagnosis and Intervention System
Intervention Lesson **B36**

oubles

Intervention Lessons
Keyed to lessons in the program

How to Use the Math Diagnosis and Intervention System

1. Assessment

Using the Diagnostic Tests For entry-level assessment, choose the appropriate diagnostic test based on whether you want to diagnose readiness by testing content that should have already been learned or you want to give a pretest on content you plan to teach. For summative evaluation, choose the test or part of a test that assesses the content you covered.

❶ Grade specific Each diagnostic test focuses on grade-specific content. Note that problem solving is integrated throughout each Diagnostic Test.

❷ Organized by booklet topics Each test is broken into parts. Each part covers content in one of Booklets A–E. You can give the entire test or just certain parts.

❸ Parallel forms Forms A and B are parallel item for item. At Grades K–3, children record responses right on the page.

❷   ❶   ❸

Name _____

Math Diagnosis and Intervention System
Grade 2 **Diagnostic Test, Form A**

Numbers, Place Value, Money, and Patterns

Mark the best answer.

1.   Which number do the

2.   Which shows thirteen?

Name _____

Math Diagnosis and Intervention System
Grade 2 **Diagnostic Test, Form B**

Numbers, Place Value, Money, and Patterns

Mark the best answer.

1.   Which number do the models show?

2.   Which shows eleven?

Ⓐ I

Ⓑ II

Ⓒ I2

Ⓓ 2I

2. Diagnosis

Using the Class Record Form The Class Record Form is a good way to get a profile on the performance of individual students as well as groups of students. When the form is completed, you can quickly "see" areas of strength and weakness for an individual (by looking across a row) or for groups of students (by looking down the columns).

❶ Use with Form A or Form B You can use the Class Record Form to record results on Form A or Form B of the Diagnostic Test.

❷ Mark items missed For each student, mark items missed in the appropriate columns.

❸ Record scores Write the total number correct for each part of the test and for the entire test. Circle scores that fall below the proficiency level of 66%. Use a different proficiency level if you wish.

❹ Interpret results If a student's score for part or all of the test falls below the proficiency level, give part or all of the diagnostic test for the previous grade. Then use the results to make informed decisions about placement or intervention for that student. Sometimes a group of students or an entire class can benefit from the same intervention. If you're giving the test as a pretest and a student, group of students, or the whole class does quite well on part of a test, consider skipping that topic for those students or covering it quickly.

Date _____

Grade 2 Diagnostic Test Form A _____ or Form B _____

Math Diagnosis and Intervention System
Grade 2 Class Record Form

	Numbers, Place Value, Money, and Patterns					Basic Facts														
	Greater Numbers, Comparing, and Ordering				Number correct for items 1–18. Circle if less than 12.	Addition and Subtraction: Basic Facts to 12								Addition and Subtraction: Basic Facts to 20						
	A81–A84					B7, B9, B11, B17, B22								B25–B27, B30, B32–B34, B36–B38						
	15	16	17	18		19	20	21	22	23	24	25	26	27	28	29	30	31	32	33
			X		12/18	X			X			X				X			X	
1					___/18															
2					___/18															
3					___/18															
4					___/18															
5					___/18															
6					___/18															

3. Intervention

Using the Intervention Lessons With these resources, you can provide intervention on a few topics or as many topics as needed.

Intervention during school Provide intervention after specific lessons or at the end of a topic.

Intervention in after-school, Saturday-school, or summer-school (intersession) programs Use the Intervention Lessons that focus on areas of weakness. If there are many areas of weakness, prioritize pages that cover those areas. Or, in summer school, 1–2 Intervention Lessons can be covered per day.

Students can catch up faster if they work on pages independently at home as well as in school.

❶ Intervention Lesson For Grades K, 1, and 2, an Intervention Lesson consists of a teacher-directed activity followed by problems. In a Grade 3 Intervention Lesson, the student will first answer a series of questions that guide him or her to the correct answer of a given problem. This is followed by additional, but similar, problems.

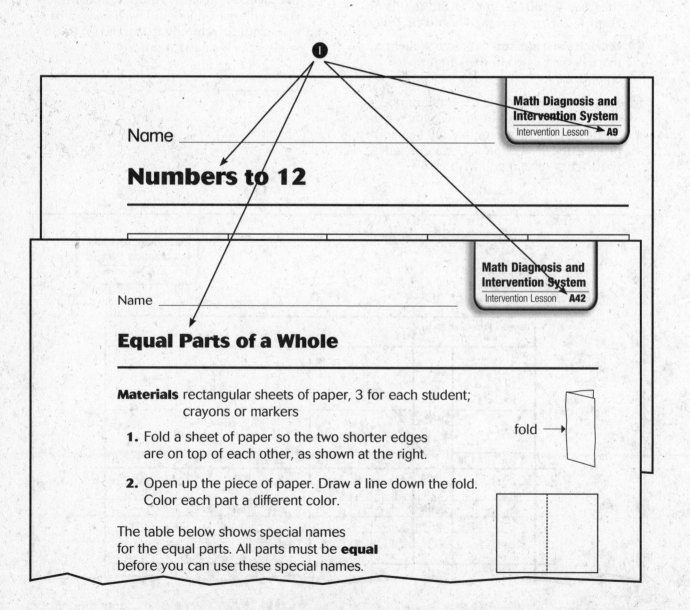

Name

Numbers to 12

Math Diagnosis and Intervention System
Intervention Lesson ▸ A9

Name

Equal Parts of a Whole

Math Diagnosis and Intervention System
Intervention Lesson A42

Materials rectangular sheets of paper, 3 for each student; crayons or markers

1. Fold a sheet of paper so the two shorter edges are on top of each other, as shown at the right.

fold →

2. Open up the piece of paper. Draw a line down the fold. Color each part a different color.

The table below shows special names for the equal parts. All parts must be **equal** before you can use these special names.

4. Monitoring

Using the Individual Record Form The Individual Record Form can be used for students who need occasional intervention during the year. It can be used with students who are one to two standard deviations below the mean on standardized tests and need additional work beyond the regular class. The Individual Record Form is particularly helpful when working with students who are at risk of failing and whose progress requires careful documentation and communication.

❶ Use with Form A or Form B You can use the Individual Record Form to record results on Form A or Form B of the Diagnostic Test.

❷ Indicate items missed Circle test items missed.

❸ Record scores Write the total number correct for each part of the test and for the entire test. Circle scores that fall below the proficiency level of 66%. Use a different proficiency level if you wish.

❹ Record intervention assignments Cross out to indicate Intervention Lessons you assign.

❺ Communicate with parents and helpers Use the form at parent conferences. You might have students and parents record assignments as they are completed. Pass the form along to tutors or others who are helping the student.

Student Name _____

Math Diagnosis and Intervention System
Grade 2 **Individual Record Form**

Topic	Grade 2 Content	Assessment and Diagnosis			Intervention
		Circle (○) items missed on Grade 2 Diagnostic Test Form A ___ or B ___	OK score (66% or greater)	Actual score. Circle if not OK.	Circle (○) Intervention Lessons assigned.
Numbers, Place Value, Money, and Patterns	Numbers and Place Value to 100	1 2 3 4 5 6			A17 A19 A24 A27 A28 A30
	Fractions	7 8 9 10	12/18	___/18	A35 A38 A39 A40
	Money and Decimals	11 12 13 14			A57 A60 A62 A63
	Greater Numbers, Comparing, and Ordering	15 16 17 18			A81 A82 A83 A84
Basic Facts	Addition and Subtraction: Basic Facts to 12	19 20 21 22 23			B7 B9 B11 B17 B22
	Addition and Subtraction: Basic Facts to 20	24 25 26 27 28 29 30 31 32 33	15/22	___/22	B25 B26 B27 B30 B32 B33 B34 B36 B37 B38
	Multiplication and Division Facts and Properties	34 35 36 37 38 39 40			B43 B44 B46 B57

Step Up to the Next Grade

You can use the *Math Diagnosis and Intervention System* to help prepare students for the next grade. You might want to do this at the end of the school year, after students have completed the lessons in the Student Edition and taken a major test on those lessons.

See the Pacing Guide on page T11 of your Overview and Implementation Guide. The Pacing Guide shows that you can complete the Student Edition lessons in about 20 school days before the end of the school year.

Here are suggestions for 20 lessons in the *Math Diagnosis and Intervention System* that you might want to use during those 20 days.

Current grade	Lessons in the *Math Diagnosis and Intervention System* to help prepare students for the next grade
Grade K	A7, A13, A16, A17, A19, B7, B12, B14, B15, B16, C1, C2, C3, C5, C14, D5, D6, D51, D52, D72
Grade 1	A29, A32, A41, A61, A86, B23, B32, B33, B44, B47, C8, C12, C13, C22, C31, D25, D26, D50, D51, D89
Grade 2	A42, A43, A47, A48, A74, B45, B48, B56, B62, B63, C26, C27, C28, C29, C37, D59, D62, D63, D64, D65
Grade 3	F8, F9, F10, F11, F29, G7, G42, G59, G66, G67, H1, H2, H3, H14, H18, I8, I10, I11, I13, I45
Grade 4	F19, F33, F34, F40, F43, G60, G63, G65, G73, G75, H19, H24, H31, H42, H46, I17, I20, I33, I36, I49
Grade 5	F18, F21, F41, F52, F54, F55, G58, H42, H49, H72, H80, H84, I37, I58, I70, I86, I87, J7, J17, J30
Grade 6	Use *Step Up to Grade 7 Resources* in the Digital Teacher's Edition

Using the Math Diagnosis and Intervention System in Summer School

The plan outlined below is a suggestion to teachers on how the Math Diagnosis and Intervention System might be used during a summer-school session. Teachers may wish to alter the plan to meet the specific needs of their students.

For the purpose of this explanation, the students attending summer school will be students who have unsuccessfully completed Grade 3.

❶ First, identify the area(s) of weakness to be targeted.

- Administer the grade-level-appropriate Diagnostic Test to each student. The sample students will take Diagnostic Test Grade 3, Form A.

- Complete the Class Record Form and analyze the results of the test to identify any area(s) of weakness across the class.

- Group students who need help with the same mathematical concepts.

❷ Then determine the grade level at which intervention should begin.

- Administer Diagnostic Test, Grade 2, Form A to each student. Have students focus on only the questions related to his or her particular area(s) of weakness.

- Complete a Grade 2 Individual Record Form for each student, addressing only his or her area(s) of weakness.

- If the student "passes" the portion of the Grade 2 test with respect to the area identified as his or her weakness, then intervention should begin at the Grade 3 level.

- If a Grade 3 student did not "pass" the Grade 2 test in the area of his or her weakness, then that student should be given the Grade 1 Diagnostic Test Form A. If the student "passes" the Grade 1 test, then intervention should begin at the Grade 2 level.

- The above process should continue until the student successfully answers the area-specific questions at a particular grade level. Then intervention should begin at the next higher grade level.

❸ Assign intervention and re-assess.

- Check the Table of Contents of the appropriate booklet (A–E) for the grade specific Intervention Lesson.

- Assign students the Intervention Lessons for reteaching purposes.

- Now give the student Form B of the last Diagnostic Test he or she has taken.

- If the student passes, he or she is ready for the next level of Intervention on the concept. If the student does not pass, repeat the Intervention Lesson.

❹ Complete Individual Record Forms.

- You may wish to complete an Individual Record Form for each student. These can be sent to the student's next classroom teacher to inform the teacher of the work done in summer school. You may wish to use the correlation information on the form to indicate content that students have mastered or which may require additional work.

Correlation of Student Book to
Math Diagnosis and Intervention System

		The same content is taught in the enVisionMath Program			
Booklet A	**Numbers, Place Value, Money, and Patterns**	**Gr. K**	**Gr. 1**	**Gr. 2**	**Gr. 3**

Numbers, Place Value, Money, and Patterns

		Gr. K	Gr. 1	Gr. 2	Gr. 3
A1	Zero to Five	4-1 to 4-6,	1-1		
A2	More and Fewer	4-7			
A3	Six to Ten	5-1 to 5-9	1-2		
A4	Comparing Numbers	6-1	2-1		
A5	11 to 19	12-1 to 12-4	10-2		
A6	Numbers to 30				
A7	Counting by 10s to 100	12-8	10-3		
A8	Counting to 100	12-6			
A9	Numbers to 12	12-1	1-3		
A10	Spatial Patterns for Numbers to 10		1-4, 1-5		
A11	Comparing Numbers to 10	6-3	2-1		
A12	Ordering Numbers to 12		2-2		
A13	Ordering Numbers to 12 with a Number Line		2-3		
A14	Making Numbers 11 to 20		10-1		
A15	Using Numbers 11 to 20		10-2		
A16	Using Skip Counting		10-5		
A17	Odd and Even		10-6	4-9	
A18	Counting from Any Number				
A19	Before, After, and Between		12-6	4-6	
A20	Counting with Tens and Ones		11-1		
A21	Estimating with Groups of 10				
A22	Ordinal Numbers Through Tenth				
A23	Tens		11-2	4-1	
A24	Tens and Ones		11-3	4-2	
A25	Number Patterns to 100		10-4		
A26	1 More or Less, 10 More or Less		12-1		
A27	Using >, <, and = to Compare Numbers		12-3	4-4, 4-5	
A28	Ordering Three Numbers		12-7	4-7	
A29	Number Words to Twenty			4-3	
A30	Number Words			4-3	
A31	Ordinal Numbers		10-7		
A32	Numbers to 100 on the Number Line				
A33	Number Line Estimation		12-5		

Fractions

		Gr. K	Gr. 1	Gr. 2	Gr. 3
A34	Halves				
A35	Equal Parts		19-1	12-1	
A36	Understanding Fractions to Fourths			12-2	
A37	Fractions of a Set				
A38	Writing Fractions for Part of a Region			12-3	
A39	Writing Fractions for Part of a Set				
A40	Estimating Fractions			12-4	12-4
A41	Understanding One as a Fraction				
A42	Equal Parts of a Whole		19-2		12-1
A43	Parts of a Region				12-2
A44	Parts of a Set		19-3, 19-4		12-3
A45	Fractions and Length				
A46	Fractions on the Number Line				12-7

Correlation of Student Book to
Math Diagnosis and Intervention System

		The same content is taught in the enVisionMath Program			
Booklet A continued		Gr. K	Gr. 1	Gr. 2	Gr. 3
A47	Using Models to Compare Fractions				12-6
A48	Using Models to Find Equivalent Fractions				12-5
A49	Equivalent Fractions				12-5
A50	Comparing Fractions on the Number Line				12-7
A51	Comparing Fractions				
A52	Adding Fractions with Like Denominators				12-8
A53	Subtracting Fractions with Like Denominators				12-9
Money and Decimals					
A54	Money				
A55	Pennies and Nickels		13-1		
A56	Dimes		13-2		
A57	Counting Pennies, Nickels, and Dimes			5-1	
A58	Quarters		13-3	5-2	
A59	Half-Dollars		13-4	5-2	
A60	Counting Sets of Coins		13-5	5-3	
A61	Comparing Sets of Coins				
A62	Ways to Show the Same Amount			5-4	
A63	Dollars			5-5	
A64	Fractions and Decimals				13-1
A65	Using Money to Understand Decimals				1-7
A66	Counting Money				1-8
A67	Making Change				13-2
Patterns					
A68	Patterns	3-1 to 3-3			
A69	Describing Patterns		9-1		
A70	Using Patterns to Predict	3-6	9-2		
A71	Extending Shape Patterns		9-3		
A72	Translating Patterns				
A73	Find a Rule				
A74	Repeating Patterns				9-1
A75	Number Patterns				9-2
A76	Input/Output Tables				9-3, 9-4
A77	Geometric Growth Patterns				9-6
A78	Translating Words to Expressions				9-5
Greater Numbers, Comparing, and Ordering					
A79	Counting by Hundreds				
A80	Building Numbers to 999			17-1	
A81	Reading and Writing Numbers to 999			17-3	
A82	Changing Numbers by Hundreds and Tens			17-4	
A83	Patterns with Numbers on Hundreds Charts			17-5	
A84	Comparing Numbers to 999			17-6	
A85	Before, After, and Between			17-7	
A86	Ordering Numbers to 999			17-8	
A87	Numbers to 999 on the Number Line				
A88	Skip Counting on the Number Line				1-1
A89	Ways to Show Numbers				
A90	Rounding to Nearest Ten and Hundred			2-4	

Correlation of Student Book to
Math Diagnosis and Intervention System

		The same content is taught in the enVisionMath Program			
Booklet A continued		Gr. K	Gr. 1	Gr. 2	Gr. 3
A91	Reading and Writing 4-Digit Numbers				1-2, 1-3
A92	Numbers Halfway Between and Rounding			2-4	
A93	Comparing and Ordering Numbers				1-5, 1-6
A94	Place-Value Patterns				1-4
Booklet B Basic Facts					
Basic Facts					
B1	Addition	10-1, 10-2, 10-4			
B2	Subtraction	11-1			
B3	Finding Sums	10-3, 10-5, 10-6	3-4	1-1	
B4	Finding Differences	11-2, 11-4 to 11-6	4-4	1-3	
B5	Making 6 and 7	5-2	3-1		
B6	Making 8 and 9	5-5	3-2, 3-3		
B7	Joining Stories		3-5	1-1	
B8	Adding Across and Down				
B9	Adding in Any Order		3-6	2-4	
B10	Parts of Ten				
B11	Adding with 0, 1, 2		6-1	2-1	
B12	Adding Doubles		6-2	2-2	
B13	Using Doubles to Add		6-3	2-3	
B14	Facts with 5 on a Ten-Frame		6-4		
B15	Making 10 on a Ten-Frame		5-3, 6-5	2-6, 2-7	
B16	Missing Parts		4-1 to 4-3	3-5	
B17	Separating Stories	11-1	4-5	1-3	
B18	Comparing Stories	11-3	4-6	1-3	
B19	Relating Addition and Subtraction		4-7, 7-2	1-6	
B20	Missing Parts of 10		5-4	3-5	
B21	Subtracting Across and Down				
B22	Subtracting with 0, 1, and 2		7-1	3-1	
B23	Using Doubles to Subtract			3-2	
B24	Thinking Addition to 12 to Subtract		7-4	3-3	
Addition and Subtraction: Basic Facts to 20					
B25	Stories about Joining			1-2	
B26	Doubles to 18		16-1	2-2	
B27	Using Doubles to Add		16-2	2-3	
B28	Adding 10				
B29	Making 10 to Add 9		16-5	2-6	
B30	Making 10 to Add 7 and 8		16-6	2-7	
B31	Adding Three Numbers		16-7	2-5	
B32	Stories about Separating			1-4	
B33	Stories about Comparing			1-5	
B34	Relating Addition and Subtraction to 18		17-1	1-6	
B35	Fact Families		17-2		
B36	Thinking Addition to Subtract Doubles		17-3		
B37	Using Addition to 18 to Subtract		17-3	3-4	
B38	Finding the Missing Part			3-2, 3-5	

Correlation of Student Book to
Math Diagnosis and Intervention System

			The same content is taught in the enVisionMath Program			
Booklet B continued		Gr. K	Gr. 1	Gr. 2	Gr. 3
B39	Using Subtraction Strategies		17-4		
B40	Subtraction Facts with 10				
B41	Addition Properties				2-1
B42	Relating Addition and Subtraction				3-1
Multiplication and Division Facts and Properties					
B43	Multiplication as Repeated Addition			19-1	5-1
B44	Arrays and Multiplication			19-2, 19-5	5-2
B45	Using Multiplication to Compare				5-3
B46	Writing Multiplication Stories			19-3	5-4
B47	Multiplying by 2 and 5				5-6
B48	Multiplying by 9				5-8
B49	Multiplying by 1 or 0				5-9
B50	Multiplying by 3				6-1
B51	Multiplying by 4				6-2
B52	Multiplying by 6 or 7				6-3
B53	Multiplying by 8				6-4
B54	Multiplying by 10				5-7
B55	Multiplying by 11 and 12				6-5
B56	Multiplying Three Numbers				6-6
B57	Meanings for Division			20-1, 20-2	7-1, 7-3
B58	Writing Division Stories			20-3	7-4
B59	Relating Multiplication and Division			20-4	8-1
B60	Dividing by 2 Through 5				8-2
B61	Dividing by 6 and 7				8-3
B62	Dividing by 8 and 9				8-4
B63	0 and 1 in Division				8-5
Booklet C	**Computation with Whole Numbers**				
Computation					
C1	Adding Tens		20-1	6-1	
C2	Adding on a Hundred Chart		20-2	6-4	
C3	Adding Tens to a Two-Digit Number		20-3	6-3	
C4	Adding Two-Digit Numbers		20-4	6-3	
C5	Estimating Sums			10-2	
C6	Regrouping in Addition			8-1	
C7	Deciding When to Regroup in Addition				
C8	Adding Two-Digit and One-Digit Numbers			8-2, 8-3	
C9	Adding with Regrouping			8-4	
C10	Two-Digit Addition			8-5	
C11	Adding Three Numbers			8-6	
C12	Subtracting Tens			7-1	
C13	Finding Parts of 100			7-2	
C14	Subtracting on a Hundred Chart		20-5	7-3	
C15	Adding on to Subtract			7-4	
C16	Subtracting Tens from a Two-Digit Number		20-6		
C17	Subtracting Two-Digit Numbers		20-7		
C18	Estimating Differences			10-5	
C19	Subtracting Two-Digit and One-Digit Numbers			9-1, 9-2, 9-3	
C20	Deciding When to Regroup in Subtraction				

Correlation of Student Book to
Math Diagnosis and Intervention System

Correlation of Student Book to Math Diagnosis and Intervention System

		The same content is taught in the enVisionMath Program			
Booklet D continued		**Gr. K**	**Gr. 1**	**Gr. 2**	**Gr. 3**
D9	Time Before and After the Hour			15-2	
D10	Equivalent Times				
D11	Comparing Temperatures		14-13		
D12	Measuring Temperature			15-5	
D13	Time to the Quarter Hour				17-1
D14	Telling Time				17-2
D15	Units of Time				17-3
D16	Elapsed Time				17-4
D17	Temperature				17-5
Length, Capacity, Weight, Area, and Volume					
D18	Comparing and Ordering by Length	9-2, 9-3	14-1		
D19	Comparing and Ordering by Capacity	9-6			
D20	Comparing and Ordering by Weight	9-8	14-10		
D21	Comparing Areas				
D22	Unit Size and Measuring	9-4	14-2		
D23	Inches and Feet		14-4		
D24	Inches, Feet, and Yards			13-4	
D25	Inches				
D26	Centimeters and Meters			13-5	
D27	Centimeters		14-5		
D28	Exploring Capacity	9-7	14-7	14-1, 14-2	
D29	Cups, Pints, and Quarts		14-8	14-3	
D30	Liters		14-9	14-4	
D31	Estimating and Measuring Weight	9-9		14-5	
D32	Pounds		14-11		
D33	Pounds and Ounces			14-6	
D34	Grams and Kilograms		14-12	14-7	
D35	Perimeter		14-6	13-6	
D36	Exploring Area			13-7	
D37	Measuring Length to $\frac{1}{2}$ and $\frac{1}{4}$ Inch				14-2
D38	Using Customary Units of Length				14-3
D39	Using Metric Units of Length				15-1, 15-2
D40	Using Customary Units of Capacity				14-4
D41	Using Metric Units of Capacity				15-3
D42	Using Customary Units of Weight				14-5
D43	Using Metric Units of Mass				15-4
D44	Perimeter				16-1, 16-2
D45	Finding Area on a Grid				16-5, 16-6
D46	Counting Cubes to Find Volume				16-7
Geometry					
D47	Position and Location				
D48	Shape	7-1, 7-2	8-1		
D49	Solid Figures	7-6, 7-7	8-9		
D50	Flat Surfaces of Solid Figures	7-8		11-2	
D51	Properties of Plane Shapes		8-2		
D52	Making New Shapes from Shapes		8-3	11-3	
D53	Cutting Shapes Apart		8-4	11-4	
D54	Same Size, Same Shape		8-6	11-5	
D55	Ways to Move Shapes		8-5	11-6	

Correlation of Student Book to
Math Diagnosis and Intervention System

		The same content is taught in the enVisionMath Program			
Booklet D continued		**Gr. K**	**Gr. 1**	**Gr. 2**	**Gr. 3**
D56	Symmetry		8-7	11-7	
D57	Flat Surfaces and Corners		8-10		
D58	Faces, Corners, and Edges			11-1	
D59	Solid Figures				10-1, 10-2
D60	Breaking Apart Solids				
D61	Lines and Line Segments				10-3
D62	Acute, Right, and Obtuse Angles				10-4
D63	Polygons				10-5
D64	Classifying Triangles Using Sides and Angles				10-6
D65	Quadrilaterals				10-7
D66	Congruent Figures and Motions				11-1
D67	Line Symmetry				11-2, 11-3
Statistics, Data Analysis, and Probability					
D68	Sorting and Classifying	1-2 to 1-4			
D69	Graphing	16-1			
D70	Reading Picture Graphs	16-4	18-1, 18-2 18-6,		
D71	Reading Bar Graphs	16-5	18-2, 18-3	16-2	
D72	Tallying Results		18-5	16-3	
D73	Real Graphs		18-6		
D74	Data and Picture Graphs		18-7	16-1	
D75	Making Bar Graphs			16-3	
D76	Locations on a Grid		18-4	16-4	
D77	Range and Mode				
D78	Likely or Unlikely		18-10	16-5	
D79	Certain or Impossible				
D80	Certain, Probable, Impossible		18-9	16-6	
D81	Graphing Ordered Pairs				20-5
D82	Recording Data from a Survey				20-1
D83	Reading and Making Pictographs				20-2, 20-3
D84	Reading and Making a Bar Graph				20-2, 20-4
D85	Making Line Plots				
D86	How Likely?				20-6
D87	Outcomes and Experiments				20-7
D88	Line Plots and Probability				20-8
D89	Making Bar Graphs to Show Outcomes				

Booklet E   Problem Solving

Problem Solving Skills					
E1	Extra Information		20-8		
E2	Two-Question Problems		16-4	3-6	
E3	Multiple-Step Problems			15-6	
E4	Use Data from a Table or Graph		15-6, 19-5	4-10	
E5	Missing or Extra Information			7-5	13-5
E6	Two-Question Problems			9-7	5-10
E7	Multiple-Step Problems				6-7
E8	Multiple-Step Problems				19-6

Correlation of Student Book to
Math Diagnosis and Intervention System

Booklet E continued		The same content is taught in the enVisionMath Program			
		Gr. K	Gr. 1	Gr. 2	Gr. 3

Problem Solving Strategies

		Gr. K	Gr. 1	Gr. 2	Gr. 3
E9	Look for a Pattern	12-10	10-9	6-5	
E10	Look for a Pattern				
E11	Make a Table and Look for a Pattern			20-5	
E12	Make a Table		5-5, 16-8		
E13	Use Objects	6-5	1-6, 3-7	1-7	
E14	Act it Out	2-6	2-4		
E15	Make An Organized List		11-6, 12-8		
E16	Try, Check, Revise		13-6	10-7	
E17	Use Objects and Reasoning		14-3		
E18	Use Reasoning	1-5		11-8	
E19	Draw a Picture and Write a Number Sentence	10-7	6-6, 7-5, 17-5	2-8, 8-7	
E20	Draw a Picture and Write a Number Sentence			19-6	
E21	Make a Table and Look for a Pattern				12-10, 15-5
E22	Act It Out				7-5, 9-8, 11-4, 14-6
E23	Make an Organized List			5-6	1-9
E24	Try, Check, and Revise				16-4
E25	Draw a Picture and Write a Number Sentence				2-10, 4-6, 13-4
E26	Draw a Picture and Write a Number Sentence				18-7
E27	Draw a Picture and Write a Number Sentence				8-6
E28	Solve a Simpler Problem				16-8
E29	Make a Graph				20-9
E30	Work Backward				17-6

Reasoning and Communication

		Gr. K	Gr. 1	Gr. 2	Gr. 3
E31	Make and Test Generalizations				10-8
E32	Reasonableness				3-5
E33	Write to Explain				5-5

Student Name _____

Topic	Grade K Content	Assessment and Diagnosis			Intervention
		Circle (○) items missed on Grade 3 Diagnostic Test Form A___ or B ___	OK score (66% or greater)	Actual score. Circle if not OK.	Circle (○) Intervention Lessons assigned.
Numbers, Place Value, Money, and Patterns	Numbers and Place Value to 100	1 2 3 4 5 6 7 8 9 10 11 12 13 14 15	16/23	___/23	A1 A2 A3 A5 A7 A16 A31
	Fractions	16			A35
	Money and Decimals	17 18 19 20			A55 A56 A59
	Patterns	21 22 23			A68 A70
Basic Facts	Addition and Subtraction: Basic Fact to 12	24 25 26 27 28 29	4/6	___/6	B1 B2 B3 B18
Measurement, Geometry, Data Analysis, and Probability	Time and Temperature	30 31 32	6/9	___/9	D4 D7
	Length, Capacity, Weight, Area, and Volume	33 34 35			D18 D19
	Geometry	36 37			D47 D49
	Statistics, Data Analysis, and Probability	38			D69
Problem Solving	Problem Solving Skills	39	4/6	___/6	E4
	Problem Solving Strategies in Grades K-2	40 41 42 43 44			E9 E13 E15 E18 E19
	Total Score		30/44	___/44	

Date _____
Grade K Diagnostic Test Form A ____ or Form B ____

Directions: Indicate Form A or Form B above. For each student name, mark test items missed. Record totals for parts of the test and for the whole test. Circle totals that fall below the indicated proficiency level (66% or greater). Use a different level if you wish.

Student Name		1	2	3	4	5	6	7	8	9	10	11	12	13	14	15
		Number Place Value, Money, and Patterns														
		Numbers and Place Value to 100														
		A1-A3, A5, A7, A16, A31														
Sample					X				X		X			X		X
1																
2																
3																
4																
5																
6																
7																
8																
9																
10																
11																
12																
13																
14																
15																
16																
17																
18																
19																
20																
21																
22																
23																
24																
25																
26																
27																
28																
29																
30																

Date _____

Grade K Diagnostic Test Form A ____ or Form B ____

	Number Place Value, Money, and Patterns								Number correct for items 1–23. Circle if less than 16.
	Fractions	Money and Decimals				Patterns			
	A35	A55, A56, A59				A68, A70			
	16	17	18	19	20	21	22	23	
				X			X		_16_/23
1									__/23
2									__/23
3									__/23
4									__/23
5									__/23
6									__/23
7									__/23
8									__/23
9									__/23
10									__/23
11									__/23
12									__/23
13									__/23
14									__/23
15									__/23
16									__/23
17									__/23
18									__/23
19									__/23
20									__/23
21									__/23
22									__/23
23									__/23
24									__/23
25									__/23
26									__/23
27									__/23
28									__/23
29									__/23
30									__/23

Date _____
Grade K Diagnostic Test Form A ___ or Form B ___

Student Name	Basic Facts — Addition and Subtraction: Basic Facts to 12 (B1-B3, B18)						Number correct for items 24–29. Circle if less than 4.	Measurement, Geometry, Data Analysis, and Probability — Time and Temperature (B4, D7)			Measurement, Geometry, Data Analysis, and Probability — Length, Capacity, Weight, Area, and Volume (D18, D19)		
	24	25	26	27	28	29		30	31	32	33	34	35
Sample		X		X			4 /6	X			X		
1							__/6						
2							__/6						
3							__/6						
4							__/6						
5							__/6						
6							__/6						
7							__/6						
8							__/6						
9							__/6						
10							__/6						
11							__/6						
12							__/6						
13							__/6						
14							__/6						
15							__/6						
16							__/6						
17							__/6						
18							__/6						
19							__/6						
20							__/6						
21							__/6						
22							__/6						
23							__/6						
24							__/6						
25							__/6						
26							__/6						
27							__/6						
28							__/6						
29							__/6						
30							__/6						

Date _____
Grade K Diagnostic Test Form A ____ or Form B ____

	Measurement, Geometry, Data Analysis, and Probability				Problem Solving						
	Geometry	Statistics, Data Analysis, and Probability	Number correct for items 30–38. Circle if less than 6.		Problem Solving	Problem Solving Strategies					Number correct for items 39–44. Circle if less than 4.
	D47, D49		D69		E4	E9, E13, E15, E18, E19					
	36	37	38		39	40	41	42	43	44	
		X		6 /9	X		X				4 /6
1				__/9							__/6
2				__/9							__/6
3				__/9							__/6
4				__/9							__/6
5				__/9							__/6
6				__/9							__/6
7				__/9							__/6
8				__/9							__/6
9				__/9							__/6
10				__/9							__/6
11				__/9							__/6
12				__/9							__/6
13				__/9							__/6
14				__/9							__/6
15				__/9							__/6
16				__/9							__/6
17				__/9							__/6
18				__/9							__/6
19				__/9							__/6
20				__/9							__/6
21				__/9							__/6
22				__/9							__/6
23				__/9							__/6
24				__/9							__/6
25				__/9							__/6
26				__/9							__/6
27				__/9							__/6
28				__/9							__/6
29				__/9							__/6
30				__/9							__/6

© Pearson Education, Inc.

Correlation of enVisionMath to Math Diagnosis and Intervention System

Topics and Lessons	Intervention Lesson
1 Sorting and Classifying	
1.1 Same and Different	
1.2 Sorting by One Attribute	D68
1.3 Sorting the Same Set in Different Ways	D68
1.4 Sorting by More Than One Attribute	D68
1.5 Problem Solving: Use Logical Reasoning	E15
2 Position and Location	
2.1 Inside and Outside	
2.2 Over, Under, and On	
2.3 Top, Middle, and Bottom	
2.4 Before and After (objects)	
2.5 Left and Right	
2.6 Problem Solving: Act it Out	E14
3 Patterns	
3.1 Sound and Movement Patterns	A68
3.2 Color Patterns	A68
3.3 Shape Patterns	A68
3.4 Comparing Patterns	
3.5 Problem Solving: Look for a Pattern	
3.6 Using Patterns to Predict	A70
3.7 Creating Patterns	
4 Zero to Five	
4.1 Counting 1, 2, and 3	A1
4.2 Reading and Writing 1, 2, and 3	A1
4.3 Counting 4 and 5	A1
4.4 Reading and Writing 4 and 5	A1
4.5 Reading and Writing 0	A1
4.6 Making 4 and 5	A1
4.7 More, Fewer, and Same As	A2
4.8 1 and 2 More	
4.9 1 and 2 Fewer	
4.10 Problem Solving: Make an Organized List	

Correlation of enVisionMath to
Math Diagnosis and Intervention System

Topics and Lessons	Intervention Lesson
5 Six to Ten	
5.1 Counting 6 and 7	A3
5.2 Making 6 and 7	A3, B5
5.3 Reading and Writing 6 and 7	A3
5.4 Counting 8 and 9	A3
5.5 Making 8 and 9	A3, B6
5.6 Reading and Writing 8 and 9	A3
5.7 Counting 10	A3
5.8 Making 10	A3
5.9 Reading and Writing 10	A3
5.10 Ordering Numbers on a Number Line	
5.11 Problem Solving: Make a Graph	
6 Comparing Numbers	
6.1 Comparing Numbers Through 10	A4
6.2 Comparing Numbers to 5	
6.3 Comparing Numbers to 10	A11
6.4 1 and 2 More and Fewer	
6.5 Problem Solving: Use Objects	E13
7 Geometry	
7.1 Squares and Other Rectangles	D48
7.2 Circles and Triangles	D48
7.3 Making Shapes from Other Shapes	D52
7.4 Same Size, Same Shape (Congruence)	D54
7.5 Symmetry	D56
7.6 Solid Figures	D49
7.7 Comparing Solid Figures	D49
7.8 Flat Surfaces of Solid Figures	D50
7.9 Problem Solving: Use Objects	E13
8 Fractions and Ordinals	
8.1 Equal Parts	
8.2 Halves	A34
8.3 Problem Solving: Act It Out	
8.4 Ordinal Numbers Through Fifth	
8.5 Ordinal Numbers Through Tenth	A22
8.6 Problem Solving: Draw a Picture	

Topics and Lessons	Intervention Lesson
9 Measurement	
9.1 Comparing and Ordering by Size	
9.2 Comparing Lengths	D18
9.3 Ordering by Length	D18
9.4 Measuring Length	D22
9.5 Problem Solving: Try, Check and Revise	
9.6 Comparing Capacities	D19
9.7 Measuring Capacity	D28
9.8 Comparing Weights	D20
9.9 Measuring Weight	D31
9.10 Problem Solving: Try, Check and Revise	
10 Addition	
10.1 Stories About Joining	B1
10.2 More Joining	B1
10.3 Joining Groups	B3
10.4 Using the Plus Sign	B1
10.5 Finding Sums	B3
10.6 Addition Sentences	B3
10.7 Problem Solving: Draw a Picture	E19
11 Subtraction	
11.1 Stories About Separating	B2, B17
11.2 Stories About Take Away	B4
11.3 Stories About Comparing	B18
11.4 Using the Minus Sign	B4
11.5 Finding Differences	B4
11.6 Subtraction Sentences	B4
11.7 Problem Solving: Act it Out	
12 Larger Numbers	
12.1 Counting, Reading, and Writing 11 and 12	A5, A9
12.2 Counting, Reading, and Writing 13, 14, and 15	A5
12.3 Counting, Reading, and Writing 16 and 17	A5
12.4 Counting, Reading, and Writing 18, 19, and 20	A5
12.5 Odd and Even	
12.6 Counting to 100	A8
12.7 Patterns on a Hundred Chart	
12.8 Counting Groups of 10	A7
12.9 Skip Counting by 2 and 5	
12.10 Problem Solving: Look for a Pattern	E9

Correlation of enVisionMath to
Math Diagnosis and Intervention System

Topics and Lessons	Intervention Lesson
13 Money	
13.1 Penny	
13.2 Nickel	
13.3 Dime	
13.4 Quarter and Dollar	A54
13.5 Comparing Money	
13.6 Problem Solving: Act It Out	
14 Time	
14.1 More Time and Less Time	D1
14.2 Order of the Day	D1
14.3 Order of Events	D1
14.4 Finding Numbers on Clocks	D4
14.5 Telling Time to the Hour	D4
14.6 Times of Events	
14.7 Problem Solving: Use Reasoning	
15 Calendar	
15.1 Months and Seasons	D2
15.2 Days of the Week	D2
15.3 Yesterday, Today, and Tomorrow	D3
15.4 Numbers on a Calendar	D3
15.5 Calendar	D3
15.6 Temperature	
15.7 Problem Solving: Draw a Picture	
16 Graphing	
16.1 As Many, More, and Fewer	D69
16.2 Collecting Data	
16.3 Real Graphs	D73
16.4 Picture Graphs	D70
16.5 Bar Graphs	D71
16.6 More Likely, Less Likely	
16.7 Problem Solving: Make a Graph	

Student Name _____

Topic	Grade 1 Content	Assessment and Diagnosis			Intervention
		Circle (○) items missed on Grade 3 Diagnostic Test Form A___ or B ___	OK score (66% or greater)	Actual score. Circle if not OK.	Circle (○) Intervention Lessons assigned.
Numbers, Place Value, Money, and Patterns	Numbers and Place Value to 100	1 2 3 4 5 6 7 8 9 10 11	11/16	___/16	A3 A5 A7 A10 A16 A19 A24 A26 A31
	Fractions	12			A37
	Money and Decimals	13 14			A59 A60
	Patterns	15 16			A70 A73
Basic Facts	Addition and Subtraction: Basic Facts to 12	17 18 19 20 21 22 23 24 25 26 27 28	12/17	___/17	B3 B4 B5 B6 B11 B12 B16 B18 B20 B22 B24
	Addition and Subtraction: Basic Facts to 20	29 30 31 32 33			B27 B30 B35 B36 B37 B39
Computation with Whole Numbers	Two-Digit Addition and Subtraction	34 35 36 37 38 39 40 41	5/8	___/8	C1 C3 C4 C16 C17
Measurement, Geometry, Data Analysis, and Probability	Time and Temperature	42 43 44	7/11	___/11	D4 D6 D7
	Length, Capacity, Weight, Area, and Volume	45 46 47 48			D23 D29 D34 D35
	Geometry	49 50 51			D49 D51 D53
	Statistics, Data Analysis, and Probability	52			D72
Problem Solving	Problem Solving Skills	53	4/6	___/6	E4
	Problem Solving Strategies	54 55 56 57 58			E9 E12 E13 E16 E19
	Total Score		39/58	___/58	

Date _____
Grade 1 Diagnostic Test Form A ____ or Form B ____

Directions: Indicate Form A or Form B above. For each student name, mark test items missed. Record totals for parts of the test and for the whole test. Circle totals that fall below the indicated proficiency level (66% or greater). Use a different level if you wish.

Student Name												Numbers, Place Value, Money, and Patterns
												Numbers and Place Value to 100 / Fractions
												A3, A5, A7, A10, A16, A19, A24, A26, A31 / A37
	1	**2**	**3**	**4**	**5**	**6**	**7**	**8**	**9**	**10**	**11**	**12**
Sample				X				X		X		X
1												
2												
3												
4												
5												
6												
7												
8												
9												
10												
11												
12												
13												
14												
15												
16												
17												
18												
19												
20												
21												
22												
23												
24												
25												
26												
27												
28												
29												
30												

Date _____
Grade 1 Diagnostic Test Form A ____ or Form B ____

		Numbers, Place Value, Money, and Patterns			
		Money and Decimals		Patterns	Number correct for items 1–16. Circle if less than 11.
		A59–A60		A70, A73	
		13	14	15	16	
				X		11/16
1						__/16
2						__/16
3						__/16
4						__/16
5						__/16
6						__/16
7						__/16
8						__/16
9						__/16
10						__/16
11						__/16
12						__/16
13						__/16
14						__/16
15						__/16
16						__/16
17						__/16
18						__/16
19						__/16
20						__/16
21						__/16
22						__/16
23						__/16
24						__/16
25						__/16
26						__/16
27						__/16
28						__/16
29						__/16
30						__/16

Date _____

Grade 1 Diagnostic Test Form A ___ or Form B ___

Student Name	Basic Facts																Number correct for items 17–33. Circle if less than 11.
	Addition and Subtraction: Basic Facts to 12 — B3-B6, B11, B12, B16, B18, B20, B22, B24												Addition and Subtraction: Basic Facts to 20 — B27, B30, B35-B37, B39					
	17	18	19	20	21	22	23	24	25	26	27	28	29	30	31	32	33	
Sample	X			X				X		X		X	X					<u>11</u>/17
1																		__/17
2																		__/17
3																		__/17
4																		__/17
5																		__/17
6																		__/17
7																		__/17
8																		__/17
9																		__/17
10																		__/17
11																		__/17
12																		__/17
13																		__/17
14																		__/17
15																		__/17
16																		__/17
17																		__/17
18																		__/17
19																		__/17
20																		__/17
21																		__/17
22																		__/17
23																		__/17
24																		__/17
25																		__/17
26																		__/17
27																		__/17
28																		__/17
29																		__/17
30																		__/17

Date _____

Grade 1 Diagnostic Test Form A ___ or Form B ___

		Computation with Whole Numbers							Number correct for items 34–41. Circle if less than 5.
		Two-Digit Addition and Subtraction							
		C1-C4, C16, C17							
	34	**35**	**36**	**37**	**38**	**39**	**40**	**41**	
		X			X			X	5 /8
1									__/8
2									__/8
3									__/8
4									__/8
5									__/8
6									__/8
7									__/8
8									__/8
9									__/8
10									__/8
11									__/8
12									__/8
13									__/8
14									__/8
15									__/8
16									__/8
17									__/8
18									__/8
19									__/8
20									__/8
21									__/8
22									__/8
23									__/8
24									__/8
25									__/8
26									__/8
27									__/8
28									__/8
29									__/8
30									__/8

Student Name	Measurement, Geometry, Data Analysis, and Probability											Number correct for items 42–52. Circle if less than 17.
	Time and Temperature			Length, Capacity, Weight, Area, and Volume				Geometry			Statistics, Data Analysis, and Probability	
	D4, D6, D7			D23, D29, D34, D35				D49, D51, D53			D72	
	42	43	44	45	46	47	48	49	50	51	52	
Sample				X				X		X		_8_/11
1												__/11
2												__/11
3												__/11
4												__/11
5												__/11
6												__/11
7												__/11
8												__/11
9												__/11
10												__/11
11												__/11
12												__/11
13												__/11
14												__/11
15												__/11
16												__/11
17												__/11
18												__/11
19												__/11
20												__/11
21												__/11
22												__/11
23												__/11
24												__/11
25												__/11
26												__/11
27												__/11
28												__/11
29												__/11
30												__/11

	Problem Solving						
	Problem Solving Skills	Problem Solving Strategies					Number correct for items 53–58. Circle if less than 4.
	E4	E9, E12, E13, E16, E19					
	53	54	55	56	57	58	
		X			X		_4_ /6
1							__/6
2							__/6
3							__/6
4							__/6
5							__/6
6							__/6
7							__/6
8							__/6
9							__/6
10							__/6
11							__/6
12							__/6
13							__/6
14							__/6
15							__/6
16							__/6
17							__/6
18							__/6
19							__/6
20							__/6
21							__/6
22							__/6
23							__/6
24							__/6
25							__/6
26							__/6
27							__/6
28							__/6
29							__/6
30							__/6

Correlation of enVisionMath to Math Diagnosis and Intervention System

Topics and Lessons	Intervention Lesson
1 Numbers to 12	
1-1 0 to 5	A1
1-2 6 to 10	A3
1-3 10, 11, and 12	A9
1-4 Spatial Patterns for Numbers to 9	A10
1-5 Spatial Patterns for Numbers to 10	A10
1-6 Problem Solving: Use Objects	E13
2 Comparing and Ordering Numbers	
2-1 Comparing Two Numbers	A4, A11
2-2 Ordering Three Numbers	A12
2-3 Ordering Numbers to 12 with a Number Line	A13
2-4 Problem Solving: Act It Out	E14
3 Understanding Addition	
3-1 Making 6 and 7	
3-2 Making 8	
3-3 Making 9	
3-4 Introducing Addition Number Sentences	B3
3-5 Stories About Joining	B6
3-6 Adding in Any Order	B8
3-7 Problem Solving: Use Objects	E13
4 Understanding Subtraction	
4-1 Finding Missing Parts of 6 and 7	B16
4-2 Finding Missing Parts of 8	B16
4-3 Finding Missing Parts of 9	B16
4-4 Introducing Subtraction Number Sentences	B4
4-5 Stories About Separating	B17
4-6 Stories About Comparing	B18
4-7 Connecting Addition and Subtraction	B19
4-8 Problem Solving: Use Objects	
5 Five and Ten Relationships	
5-1 Representing Numbers on a Ten-Frame	
5-2 Recognizing Numbers on a Ten-Frame	
5-3 Parts of 10	B15
5-4 Finding Missing Parts of 10	B20
5-5 Problem Solving: Make a Table	E12

Correlation of enVisionMath to Math Diagnosis and Intervention System

Topics and Lessons	Intervention Lesson
6 Addition Facts to 12	
6-1 Adding with 0, 1, 2	B11
6-2 Doubles	B12
6-3 Near Doubles	B13
6-4 Facts with 5 on a Ten-Frame	B14
6-5 Making 10 on a Ten-Frame	B15
6-6 Problem Solving: Draw a Picture and Write a Number Sentence	E19
7 Subtraction Facts to 12	
7-1 Subtracting with 0, 1, 2	B22
7-2 Thinking Addition	B19
7-3 Thinking Addition to 8 to Subtract	
7-4 Thinking Addition to 12 to Subtract	B24
7-5 Problem Solving: Draw a Picture and Write a Number Sentence	E19
8 Geometry	
8-1 Identifying Plane Shapes	D48
8-2 Properties of Plane Shapes	D51
8-3 Making New Shapes from Shapes	D52
8-4 Breaking Apart Shapes to Make Shapes	D53
8-5 Ways to Move Shapes	
8-6 Congruence	
8-7 Symmetry	
8-8 Problem Solving: Make an Organized List	
8-9 Identifying Solid Figures	D49
8-10 Flat Surfaces and Corners	
8-11 Sorting Solid Figures	
9 Patterns	
9-1 Describing Patterns	A69
9-2 Using Patterns to Predict	A70
9-3 Extending Shape Patterns	A71
9-4 Problem Solving: Look for a Pattern	
10 Counting and Number Patterns to 100	
10-1 Making Numbers 11 to 20	A14
10-2 Using Numbers 11 to 20	A5, A15
10-3 Counting by 10s to 100	A7
10-4 Counting Patterns on a Hundred Chart	A25
10-5 Using Skip Counting	A16
10-6 Odd and Even Numbers	A17
10-7 Ordinals Through Twentieth	A31
10-8 Patterns in Tables	
10-9 Problem Solving: Look for a Pattern	E9

Topics and Lessons	Intervention Lesson
11 Tens and Ones	
11-1 Counting with Groups of 10 and Leftovers	A20
11-2 Numbers Made with Tens	A23
11-3 Tens and Ones	A24
11-4 Expanded Form	
11-5 Ways to Make Numbers	
11-6 Problem Solving: Make an Organized List	E15
12 Comparing and Ordering Numbers to 100	
12-1 1 More, 1 Less; 10 More, 10 Less	A26
12-2 Making Numbers on a Hundred Chart	
12-3 Comparing Numbers with $>$, $<$, $=$	A27
12-4 Ordering Numbers with a Hundred Chart	
12-5 Number Line Estimation	A33
12-6 Before, After, and Between	A19
12-7 Ordering Three Numbers	A28
12-8 Problem Solving: Make an Organized List	E15
13 Counting Money	
13-1 Values of Penny and Nickel	A55
13-2 Values of Penny, Nickel, and Dime	A56
13-3 Value of Quarter	A58
13-4 Values of Half Dollar and Dollar	A59
13-5 Counting Sets of Coins	A60
13-6 Problem Solving: Try, Check, Revise	E16
14 Measurement	
14-1 Comparing and Ordering by Length	D18
14-2 Using Units to Estimate and Measure Length	D22
14-3 Problem Solving: Use Reasoning	E17
14-4 Feet and Inches	D23
14-5 Centimeters	D27
14-6 Understanding Perimeter	D35
14-7 Comparing and Ordering by Capacity	D28
14-8 Cups, Pints, and Quarts	D29
14-9 Liters	D30
14-10 Comparing and Ordering by Weight	D20
14-11 Pounds	D32
14-12 Grams and Kilograms	D34
14-13 Comparing and Ordering by Temperature	D11

Correlation of enVisionMath to Math Diagnosis and Intervention System

Topics and Lessons	Intervention Lesson
15 Time	
15-1 Understanding the Hour and Minute Hands	D4
15-2 Telling and Writing Time to the Hour	D4
15-3 Telling and Writing Time to the Half Hour	D5
15-4 Estimating and Ordering Lengths of Time	D6
15-5 Using the Calendar	
15-6 Problem Solving: Use Data from a Table	E4
16 Addition Facts to 18	
16-1 Doubles	B26
16-2 Doubles Plus 1	B27
16-3 Doubles Plus 2	
16-4 Problem Solving: Two-Question Problems	E2
16-5 Making a Ten to Add 9s	B29
16-6 Making a Ten to Add 8s	B30
16-7 Adding Three Numbers	B31
16-8 Problem Solving: Make a Table	E12
17 Subtraction Facts to 18	
17-1 Using Related Facts	B34
17-2 Using Fact Families	B35
17-3 Using Addition to Subtract	B36, B37
17-4 Subtraction Facts	B39
17-5 Problem Solving: Draw a Picture and Write a Number Sentence	E19
18 Data and Graphs	
18-1 Using Data from Real Graphs	D70
18-2 Using Data from Picture Graphs	D70, D71
18-3 Using Data from Bar Graphs	D71
18-4 Location on a Grid	D76
18-5 Collecting Data Using Tally Marks	D72
18-6 Making Real Graphs	D70, D73
18-7 Making Picture Graphs	D74
18-8 Problem Solving: Make a Graph	
18-9 Certain or Impossible	D80
18-10 Likely or Unlikely	D78

Topics and Lessons	Intervention Lesson
19 Fractional Parts	
19-1 Making Equal Parts	A35
19-2 Describing Equal Parts of Whole Objects	
19-3 Making Parts of a Set	
19-4 Describing Parts of Sets	
19-5 Problem Solving: Draw a Picture	E4
20 Adding and Subtracting with Tens and Ones	
20-1 Adding Groups of 10	C1
20-2 Adding Tens on a Hundred Chart	C2
20-3 Adding Tens to Two-Digit Numbers	C3
20-4 Adding to a Two-Digit Number	C4
20-5 Subtracting Tens on a Hundred Chart	C14
20-6 Subtracting Tens from Two-Digit Numbers	C16
20-7 Subtracting from a Two-Digit Number	C17
20-8 Problem-Solving: Extra Information	E1

Student Name _____

Topic	Grade 2 Content	Assessment and Diagnosis			Intervention
		Circle (○) items missed on Grade 3 Diagnostic Test Form A__ or B __	OK score (66% or greater)	Actual score. Circle if not OK.	Circle (○) Intervention Lessons assigned.
Numbers, Place Value, Money, and Patterns	Numbers and Place Value to 100	1 2 3 4 5 6	12/18	___/18	A17 A19 A24 A27 A28 A30
	Fractions	7 8 9 10			A35 A38 A39 A40
	Money and Decimals	11 12 13 14			A57 A60 A62 A63
	Greater Numbers, Comparing, and Ordering	15 16 17 18			A81 A82 A83 A84
Basic Facts	Addition and Subtraction: Basic Facts to 12	19 20 21 22 23	15/22	___/22	B7 B9 B11 B17 B22
	Addition and Subtraction: Basic Facts to 20	24 25 26 27 28 29 30 31 32 33			B25 B26 B27 B30 B32 B33 B34 B36 B37 B38
	Multiplication and Division Facts and Properties	34 35 36 37 38 39 40			B43 B44 B46 B57 B58 B59
Computation with Whole Numbers	Two-Digit Addition and Subtraction	41 42 43 44 45 46 47 48 49 50 51 52 53	12/18	___/18	C2 C4 C6 C9 C10 C12 C13 C14 C15 C19 C21 C22 C23
	Addition and Subtraction of Greater Numbers	54 55 56 57 58			C30 C31 C32 C33 C34
Measurement, Geometry, Data Analysis, and Probability	Time and Temperature	59 60 61 62 63	13/19	___/19	D6 D7 D8 D9 D12
	Length, Capacity, Weight, Area, and Volume	64 65 66 67			D22 D25 D27 D35
	Geometry	68 69 70 71 72			D50 D52 D53 D56 D58
	Statistics, Data Analysis, and Probability	73 74 75 76 77			D70 D71 D74 D76 D80
Problem Solving	Problem Solving Skills	78 79 80 81	7/10	___/10	E1 E2 E3 E4
	Problem Solving Strategies in Grades K-2	82 83 84 85 86 87			E10 E11 E15 E16 E17 E19
	Total Score		59/87	___/87	

Date _____

Grade 2 Diagnostic Test Form A ___ or Form B ___

Directions: Indicate Form A or Form B above. For each student name, mark test items missed. Record totals for parts of the test and for the whole test. Circle totals that fall below the indicated proficiency level (66% or greater). Use a different level if you wish.

Student Name	Numbers, Place Value, Money, and Patterns													
	Numbers and Place Value to 100						Fractions				Money and Decimals		
	A17, A19, A24, A27, A28, A30						A35, A38, A39, A40				A57, A60, A62, A63		
	1	2	3	4	5	6	7	8	9	10	11	12	13	14
Sample				X				X		X		X	X	
1														
2														
3														
4														
5														
6														
7														
8														
9														
10														
11														
12														
13														
14														
15														
16														
17														
18														
19														
20														
21														
22														
23														
24														
25														
26														
27														
28														
29														
30														

Date _____

Grade 2 Diagnostic Test Form A ___ or Form B ___

	Numbers, Place Value, Money, and Patterns					Basic Facts														
	Greater Numbers, Comparing, and Ordering				Number correct for items 1–18. Circle if less than 12.	Addition and Subtraction: Basic Facts to 12					Addition and Subtraction: Basic Facts to 20									
	A81–A84					B7, B9, B11, B17, B22					B25–B27, B30, B32–B34, B36–B38									
	15	16	17	18		19	20	21	22	23	24	25	26	27	28	29	30	31	32	33
			X		12/18	X			X			X				X			X	
1					__/18															
2					__/18															
3					__/18															
4					__/18															
5					__/18															
6					__/18															
7					__/18															
8					__/18															
9					__/18															
10					__/18															
11					__/18															
12					__/18															
13					__/18															
14					__/18															
15					__/18															
16					__/18															
17					__/18															
18					__/18															
19					__/18															
20					__/18															
21					__/18															
22					__/18															
23					__/18															
24					__/18															
25					__/18															
26					__/18															
27					__/18															
28					__/18															
29					__/18															
30					__/18															

Date _____
Grade 2 Diagnostic Test Form A ___ or Form B ___

Student Name			Basic Facts					
	Multiplication and Division Facts and Properties B43, B44, B46, B57–B59							Number correct for items 19–40. Circle if less than 15.
	34	35	36	37	38	39	40	
Sample				X			X	15 /22
1								__/22
2								__/22
3								__/22
4								__/22
5								__/22
6								__/22
7								__/22
8								__/22
9								__/22
10								__/22
11								__/22
12								__/22
13								__/22
14								__/22
15								__/22
16								__/22
17								__/22
18								__/22
19								__/22
20								__/22
21								__/22
22								__/22
23								__/22
24								__/22
25								__/22
26								__/22
27								__/22
28								__/22
29								__/22
30								__/22

Date _____

Grade 2 Diagnostic Test Form A ____ or Form B ____

				Computation with Whole Numbers														Number correct for items 41–58. Circle if less than 12.
				Two-Digit Addition and Subtraction										Addition and Subtraction of Greater Numbers				
				C2, C4, C6, C9, C10, C12–C15, C19, C21–C23									C30–C34				
	41	42	43	44	45	46	47	48	49	50	51	52	53	54	55	56	57	58	
			X			X			X			X			X			X	12/18
1																			__/18
2																			__/18
3																			__/18
4																			__/18
5																			__/18
6																			__/18
7																			__/18
8																			__/18
9																			__/18
10																			__/18
11																			__/18
12																			__/18
13																			__/18
14																			__/18
15																			__/18
16																			__/18
17																			__/18
18																			__/18
19																			__/18
20																			__/18
21																			__/18
22																			__/18
23																			__/18
24																			__/18
25																			__/18
26																			__/18
27																			__/18
28																			__/18
29																			__/18
30																			__/18

Student Name	Measurement, Geometry, Data Analysis, and Probability													
	Time and Temperature					Length, Capacity, Weight, Area, and Volume				Geometry				
	D6–D9, D12					D22, D25, D27, D35				D50, D52, D53, D56, D58				
	59	60	61	62	63	64	65	66	67	68	69	70	71	72
Sample				X			X				X		X	
1														
2														
3														
4														
5														
6														
7														
8														
9														
10														
11														
12														
13														
14														
15														
16														
17														
18														
19														
20														
21														
22														
23														
24														
25														
26														
27														
28														
29														
30														

Date _____
Grade 2 Diagnostic Test Form A ___ or Form B ___

	Measurement, Geometry, Data Analysis, and Probability						Problem Solving									
	Statistics, Data Analysis, and Probability					Number correct for items 59–77. Circle if less than 13.	Problem Solving Skills				Problem Solving Strategies						Number correct for items 78–87. Circle if less than 7.
	D70, D71, D74, D76, D80						E1–E4				E10, E11, E15–E17, E19						
	73	74	75	76	77		78	79	80	81	82	83	84	85	86	87	
			X			14/19	X					X				X	7/10
1						__/19											__/10
2						__/19											__/10
3						__/19											__/10
4						__/19											__/10
5						__/19											__/10
6						__/19											__/10
7						__/19											__/10
8						__/19											__/10
9						__/19											__/10
10						__/19											__/10
11						__/19											__/10
12						__/19											__/10
13						__/19											__/10
14						__/19											__/10
15						__/19											__/10
16						__/19											__/10
17						__/19											__/10
18						__/19											__/10
19						__/19											__/10
20						__/19											__/10
21						__/19											__/10
22						__/19											__/10
23						__/19											__/10
24						__/19											__/10
25						__/19											__/10
26						__/19											__/10
27						__/19											__/10
28						__/19											__/10
29						__/19											__/10
30						__/19											__/10

© Pearson Education, Inc.

Correlation of enVisionMath to Math Diagnosis and Intervention System

Topics and Lessons	Intervention Lesson
1 Understanding Addition and Subtraction	
1.1 Writing Addition Number Sentences	B3, B7
1.2 Stories About Joining	B25
1.3 Writing Subtraction Number Sentences	B4, B17, B18
1.4 Stories About Separating	B32
1.5 Stories About Comparing	B33
1.6 Connecting Addition and Subtraction	B19, B34
1.7 Problem Solving: Use Objects	E13
2 Addition Strategies	
2.1 Adding 0, 1, 2	B11
2.2 Doubles	B12, B26
2.3 Near Doubles	B13, B27
2.4 Adding in Any Order	
2.5 Adding Three Numbers	B31
2.6 Making a 10 to Add 9	B15, B29
2.7 Making a 10 to Add 8	B15, B30
2.8 Problem Solving: Draw a Picture and Write a Number Sentence	E19
3 Subtraction Strategies	
3.1 Subtracting 0, 1, 2	B22
3.2 Thinking Addition to Subtract Doubles	B23, B38
3.3 Thinking Addition to 10 to Subtract	B24
3.4 Thinking Addition to 18 to Subtract	B37
3.5 Finding the Missing Part	B16, B20, B38
3.6 Problem Solving: Two-Question Problems	B9, E2
4 Place Value: Numbers to 100	
4.1 Models for Tens	A23
4.2 Models for Tens and Ones	A24
4.3 Reading and Writing Numbers	A29, A30
4.4 Using Models to Compare Numbers	A27
4.5 Using Symbols to Compare Numbers	A27
4.6 Before, After, and Between	A19
4.7 Order Numbers	A28
4.8 Number Patterns on the Hundred Chart	
4.9 Even and Odd Numbers	A17
4.10 Problem Solving: Use Data from a Chart	E4

Correlation of enVisionMath to Math Diagnosis and Intervention System

Topics and Lessons	Intervention Lesson
5 Counting Money	
5.1 Dime, Nickel, and Penny	A56
5.2 Quarter and Half-Dollar	A57, A58
5.3 Counting Collections of Coins	A59
5.4 Ways to Show the Same Amount	A61
5.5 One Dollar	A62
5.6 Problem Solving: Make an Organized List	E23
6 Mental Addition	
6.1 Adding Tens	C1
6.2 Adding Ones	
6.3 Adding Tens and Ones	C3, C4
6.4 Adding on the Hundred Chart	C2
6.5 Problem Solving: Look for a Pattern	E9
7 Mental Subtraction	
7.1 Subtracting Tens	C12
7.2 Finding Parts of 100	C13
7.3 Subtracting on the Hundred Chart	C14
7.4 Adding On to Subtract	C15
7.5 Problem Solving: Missing or Extra Information	E5
8 Adding Two-Digit Numbers	
8.1 Regrouping 10 Ones for 1 Ten	C6
8.2 Models to Add Two- and One-Digit Numbers	C8
8.3 Adding Two- and One-Digit Numbers	C8
8.4 Models to Add Two-Digit Numbers	C9
8.5 Adding Two-Digit Numbers	C10
8.6 Adding Three Numbers	C11
8.7 Problem Solving: Draw a Picture and Write a Number Sentence	E19
9 Subtracting Two-Digit Numbers	
9.1 Regrouping 1 Ten for 10 Ones	C19
9.2 Models to Subtract Two- and One-Digit Numbers	C19
9.3 Subtracting Two- and One-Digit Numbers	C19
9.4 Models to Subtract Two-Digit Numbers	C21
9.5 Subtracting Two-Digit Numbers	C22
9.6 Using Addition to Check Subtraction	C23
9.7 Problem Solving: Two-Question Problems	E6

Topics and Lessons	Intervention Lesson
10 Using Addition and Subtraction	
10.1 Adding Money	
10.2 Estimating Sums	C5
10.3 Ways to Add	
10.4 Subtracting Money	
10.5 Estimating Differences	C18
10.6 Ways to Subtract	
10.7 Problem Solving: Try, Check, and Revise	E16
11 Geometry	
11.1 Flat Surfaces, Vertices, and Edges	D58
11.2 Relating Plane Shapes to Solid Figures	D50
11.3 Making New Shapes	D52
11.4 Cutting Shapes Apart	D53
11.5 Congruence	D54
11.6 Ways to Move Shapes	D55
11.7 Symmetry	D56
11.8 Problem Solving: Use Reasoning	E18
12 Fractions	
12.1 Wholes and Equal Parts	A35
12.2 Unit Fractions and Regions	A36
12.3 Non-Unit Fractions and Regions	A38
12.4 Estimating Fractional Parts of a Whole	A40
12.5 Fractions of a Set	
12.6 Problem Solving: Use Objects	
13 Measurement: Length and Area	
13.1 Thinking About Attributes	
13.2 Exploring Length	
13.3 Measuring Length Using Non-Standard Units	
13.4 Inches, Feet, and Yards	D23
13.5 Centimeters and Meters	D26
13.6 Exploring Perimeter	D35
13.7 Exploring Area	D36
13.8 Problem Solving: Use Objects	

Correlation of enVisionMath to
Math Diagnosis and Intervention System

Topics and Lessons	Intervention Lesson
14 Measurement: Capacity and Weight	
14.1 Exploring Capacity	D28
14.2 Measuring Capacity Using Non-Standard Units	D28
14.3 Cups, Pints, and Quarts	D29
14.4 Liters	D30
14.5 Exploring Weight	D31
14.6 Ounces and Pounds	D33
14.7 Grams and Kilograms	D34
14.8 Problem Solving: Use Objects	
15 Time and Temperature	
15.1 Telling Time to Five Minutes	D8
15.2 Telling Time Before and After the Hour	D9
15.3 Estimating Time	D6
15.4 Using a Calendar	D7
15.5 Temperature: Fahrenheit and Celsius	D12
15.6 Problem Solving: Multiple-Step Problems	E3
16 Graphs and Probability	
16.1 Organizing Data	D74
16.2 Pictographs	D71
16.3 Bar Graphs	D72, D75
16.4 Coordinate Graphs	D76
16.5 Likely and Unlikely	D78
16.6 Certain, Probable, and Impossible	D80
16.7 Problem Solving: Use a Graph	
17 Numbers and Patterns to 1,000	
17.1 Building 1,000	A79
17.2 Counting Hundreds, Tens, and Ones	
17.3 Reading and Writing Numbers to 1,000	A80
17.4 Changing Numbers by Hundreds and Tens	A81
17.5 Patterns with Numbers on a Hundred Chart	A83
17.6 Comparing Numbers	A84
17.7 Before, After, and Between	A85
17.8 Ordering Numbers	A86
17.9 Problem Solving: Look for a Pattern	

Correlation of enVisionMath to
Math Diagnosis and Intervention System

Math Diagnosis and Intervention System
Grade 2 **Correlation**

Topics and Lessons	Intervention Lesson
18 Three-Digit Addition and Subtraction	
18.1 Mental Math	C32
18.2 Estimating Sums	C30, C33
18.3 Models for Adding with Three-Digit Numbers	
18.4 Adding Three-Digit Numbers	C33
18.5 Mental Math: Ways to Find Missing Parts	
18.6 Estimating Differences	C31
18.7 Models for Subtracting with Three-Digit Numbers	C34
18.8 Subtracting Three-Digit Numbers	C34
18.9 Problem Solving: Make a Graph	
19 Multiplication Concepts	
19.1 Repeated Addition and Multiplication	B43
19.2 Building Arrays	B44
19.3 Writing Multiplication Stories	B46
19.4 Vertical Form	
19.5 Multiplying in Any Order	B44
19.6 Problem Solving: Draw a Picture and Write a Number Sentence	E20
20 Division Concepts and Facts	
20.1 Division as Sharing	B57
20.2 Division as Repeated Subtraction	B57
20.3 Writing Division Stories	B58
20.4 Relating Multiplication and Division	B59
20.5 Problem Solving: Make a Table and Look for a Pattern	E11

Student Name _____

Topic	Grade 3 Content	Assessment and Diagnosis			Intervention
		Circle (○) items missed on Grade 3 Diagnostic Test Form A___ or B___	OK score (66%)	Actual score. Circle if not OK.	Circle (○) Intervention Lessons assigned.
Numbers, Place Value, Money, and Patterns	Fractions	1 2 3 4 5 6 7	16/23	___/23	A40 A42 A43 A44 A46 A47 A48 A49 A50 A52 A53
	Money and Decimals	8 9 10 11			A64 A65 A66 A67
	Patterns	12 13 14 15 16 17			A74 A75 A76 A77 A78
	Greater Numbers, Comparing, and Ordering	18 19 20 21 22 23			A89 A90 A91 A92 A93 A94
Basic Facts	Addition and Subtraction Basic Facts to 20	24 25	8/11	___/11	B41 B42
	Multiplication and Division Facts and Properties	26 27 28 29 30 31 32 33 34			B43 B44 B45 B46 B47 B48 B49 B50 B51 B52 B53 B54 B55 B56 B57 B58 B59 B60 B61 B62 B63
Computation	Two-Digit Addition and Subtraction	35 36 37	11/16	___/16	C24 C25 C26 C27 C28 C29
	Addition and Subtraction of Greater Numbers	38 39 40 41 42 43 44			C30 C31 C32 C33 C34 C35 C37 C39 C40
	Multiplying and Dividing by One-Digit Numbers	45 46 47 48 49 50			C41 C42 C43 C44 C45 C46 C47 C50 C51
Measurement and Geometry	Time and Temperature	51 52 53	12/17	___/17	D13 D14 D15 D16 D17
	Length, Capacity, Weight, Area, and Volume	54 55 56 57 58 59 60 61			D37 D38 D39 D40 D41 D42 D43 D44 D45 D46
	Geometry	62 63 64 65 66 67			D59 D61 D62 D63 D64 D65 D66 D67
Data Analysis and Probability	Statistics, Data Analysis, and Probability	68 69 70 71 72 73 74 75 76	6/9	___/9	D81 D82 D83 D84 D86 D87 D88
Problem Solving	Problem-Solving Skills	77 78	4/6	___/6	E5 E6 E7 E8
	Problem-Solving Strategies	79 80 81			E21 E22 E23 E24 E25 E26 E27 E28 E29 E30
	Reasoning and Communication	82			E31 E32 E33
	Total Score		57/82	___/82	

Date _____

Grade 3 Diagnostic Test Form A ___ or Form B ___

Directions: Indicate Form A or Form B above. For each student name, mark test items missed. Record totals for parts of the test and for the whole test. Circle totals that fall below the indicated proficiency level (66% or greater). Use a different level if you wish.

Student Name	\multicolumn{11}{c|}{Numbers, Place Value, Money, and Patterns}

	\multicolumn{7}{c|}{Fractions}	\multicolumn{4}{c|}{Money and Decimals}
	\multicolumn{7}{c|}{A40, A42 to A44, A46 to A50, A52, A53}	\multicolumn{4}{c|}{A64 to A67}
Student Name	1	2	3	4	5	6	7	8	9	10	11
Sample		X					X			X	
1											
2											
3											
4											
5											
6											
7											
8											
9											
10											
11											
12											
13											
14											
15											
16											
17											
18											
19											
20											
21											
22											
23											
24											
25											
26											
27											
28											
29											
30											

Date _____

Grade 3 Diagnostic Test Form A ___ or Form B ___

		Numbers, Place Value, Money, and Patterns										
		Patterns						Greater Numbers, Comparing, and Ordering				Number correct for items 1–23. Circle if less than 16.
		A74 to A78						A89 to A94				
		12	13	14	15	16	17	18	19	20	21	22	23	
					X							X		18 /23
1														__/23
2														__/23
3														__/23
4														__/23
5														__/23
6														__/23
7														__/23
8														__/23
9														__/23
10														__/23
11														__/23
12														__/23
13														__/23
14														__/23
15														__/23
16														__/23
17														__/23
18														__/23
19														__/23
20														__/23
21														__/23
22														__/23
23														__/23
24														__/23
25														__/23
26														__/23
27														__/23
28														__/23
29														__/23
30														__/23

Date _____

Grade 3 Diagnostic Test Form A ___ or Form B ___

Student Name	Basic Facts											Number correct for items 24–34. Circle if less than 8.	Computation		
	Addition and Subtraction Basic Facts to 20		Multiplication and Division Facts and Properties										Two-Digit Addition and Subtraction		
	B41, B42		B43 to B63										C24 to C29		
	24	25	26	27	28	29	30	31	32	33	34		35	36	37
Sample		X					X			X		8/11			X
1												__/11			
2												__/11			
3												__/11			
4												__/11			
5												__/11			
6												__/11			
7												__/11			
8												__/11			
9												__/11			
10												__/11			
11												__/11			
12												__/11			
13												__/11			
14												__/11			
15												__/11			
16												__/11			
17												__/11			
18												__/11			
19												__/11			
20												__/11			
21												__/11			
22												__/11			
23												__/11			
24												__/11			
25												__/11			
26												__/11			
27												__/11			
28												__/11			
29												__/11			
30												__/11			

Date _____
Grade 3 Diagnostic Test Form A ____ or Form B ____

		Computation												Number correct for items 35–50. Circle if less than 11.	Measurement and Geometry		
		Addition and Subtraction of Greater Numbers							Multiplying and Dividing by One-Digit Numbers						Time and Temperature		
		C30 to C35, C37, C39, C40							C41 to C47, C50, C51						D13 to D17		
	38	39	40	41	42	43	44	45	46	47	48	49	50		51	52	53
		X								X	X	X	X	⑩/16			
1														__/16			
2														__/16			
3														__/16			
4														__/16			
5														__/16			
6														__/16			
7														__/16			
8														__/16			
9														__/16			
10														__/16			
11														__/16			
12														__/16			
13														__/16			
14														__/16			
15														__/16			
16														__/16			
17														__/16			
18														__/16			
19														__/16			
20														__/16			
21														__/16			
22														__/16			
23														__/16			
24														__/16			
25														__/16			
26														__/16			
27														__/16			
28														__/16			
29														__/16			
30														__/16			

Student Name	Measurement and Geometry														Number correct for items 51–67. Circle if less than 12.
	Length, Capacity, Weight, Area, and Volume								Geometry						
	D37 to D46								D59, D61 to D67						
	54	55	56	57	58	59	60	61	62	63	64	65	66	67	
Sample	X							X				X			14/17
1															__/17
2															__/17
3															__/17
4															__/17
5															__/17
6															__/17
7															__/17
8															__/17
9															__/17
10															__/17
11															__/17
12															__/17
13															__/17
14															__/17
15															__/17
16															__/17
17															__/17
18															__/17
19															__/17
20															__/17
21															__/17
22															__/17
23															__/17
24															__/17
25															__/17
26															__/17
27															__/17
28															__/17
29															__/17
30															__/17

Date _____

Grade 3 Diagnostic Test Form A ____ or Form B ____

				Data Analysis and Probability							Number correct for items 68–76. Circle if less than 6.	Problem-Solving Skills		Problem-Solving Strategies			Reasoning and Communication	Number correct for items 77–82. Circle if less than 4.
				Statistics, Data Analysis, and Probability								E5 to E8		E21 to E30			E31 to E33	
				D81 to D84, D86 to D88														
	68	69	70	71	72	73	74	75	76			77	78	79	80	81	82	
				X					X		7/9							6/6
1											__/9							__/6
2											__/9							__/6
3											__/9							__/6
4											__/9							__/6
5											__/9							__/6
6											__/9							__/6
7											__/9							__/6
8											__/9							__/6
9											__/9							__/6
10											__/9							__/6
11											__/9							__/6
12											__/9							__/6
13											__/9							__/6
14											__/9							__/6
15											__/9							__/6
16											__/9							__/6
17											__/9							__/6
18											__/9							__/6
19											__/9							__/6
20											__/9							__/6
21											__/9							__/6
22											__/9							__/6
23											__/9							__/6
24											__/9							__/6
25											__/9							__/6
26											__/9							__/6
27											__/9							__/6
28											__/9							__/6
29											__/9							__/6
30											__/9							__/6

Correlation of enVision Math to
Math Diagnosis and Intervention System

Topics and Lessons	Intervention Lesson
1 Numeration	
1-1 Hundreds	A89
1-2 Thousands	A91
1-3 Greater Numbers	A91
1-4 Ways to Name Numbers	A94
1-5 Comparing Numbers	A93
1-6 Ordering Numbers	A93
1-7 Counting Money	A65
1-8 Making Change	A66
1-9 Make an Organized List	E23
2 Adding Whole Numbers	
2-1 Addition Meaning and Properties	B41
2-2 Adding on a Hundred Chart	C24
2-3 Using Mental Math to Add	C26, C32
2-4 Rounding	A90, A92
2-5 Estimating Sums	C30
2-6 Adding 2-Digit Numbers	C28
2-7 Models for Adding 3-Digit Numbers	C33
2-8 Adding 3-Digit Numbers	C33
2-9 Adding 3 or More Numbers	C37
2-10 Draw a Picture	E25
3 Subtraction Number Sense	
3-1 Subtraction Meanings	B42
3-2 Subtracting on a Hundred Chart	C25
3-3 Using Mental Math to Subtract	C27
3-4 Estimating Differences	C31
3-5 Reasonableness	E32
4 Subtracting Whole Numbers to Solve Problems	
4-1 Models for Subtracting 2-Digit Numbers	C29
4-2 Subtracting 2-Digit Numbers	C29
4-3 Models for Subtracting 3-Digit Numbers	C34
4-4 Subtracting 3-Digit Numbers	C34
4-5 Subtracting Across Zero	C39
4-6 Draw a Picture and Write a Number Sentence	E25

Correlation of enVision Math to
Math Diagnosis and Intervention System

Topics and Lessons	Intervention Lesson
5 Multiplication Meanings and Facts	
5-1 Multiplication as Repeated Addition	B43
5-2 Arrays and Multiplication	B44
5-3 Using Multiplication to Compare	B45
5-4 Writing Multiplication Stories	B46
5-5 Writing to Explain	E33
5-6 2 and 5 as Factors	B47
5-7 10 as a Factor	B54
5-8 9 as a Factor	B48
5-9 Multiplying with 0 and 1	B49
5-10 Two-Question Problems	E6
6 Multiplication Fact Strategies: Use Known Facts	
6-1 3 as a Factor	B50
6-2 4 as a Factor	B51
6-3 6 and 7 as Factors	B52
6-4 8 as a Factor	B53
6-5 11 and 12 as Factors	B55
6-6 Multiplying with 3 Factors	B56
6-7 Multiple-Step Problems	E7
7 Division Meanings	
7-1 Division as Sharing	B57
7-2 Understanding Remainders	
7-3 Division as Repeated Subtraction	B57
7-4 Writing Division Stories	B58
7-5 Use Objects and Draw a Picture	E22
8 Division Facts	
8-1 Relating Multiplication and Division	B59
8-2 Fact Families with 2, 3, 4, and 5	B60
8-3 Fact Families with 6 and 7	B61
8-4 Fact Families with 8 and 9	B62
8-5 Dividing with 0 and 1	B63
8-6 Draw a Picture and Write a Number Sentence	E27

Correlation of enVision Math to
Math Diagnosis and Intervention System

Topics and Lessons	Intervention Lesson
9 Patterns and Relationships	
9-1 Repeating Patterns	A74
9-2 Number Sequences	A75
9-3 Extending Tables	A76
9-4 Writing Rules for Situations	A76
9-5 Translating Words to Expressions	A78
9-6 Geometric Patterns	A77
9-7 Equal or Unequal	C40
9-8 Act It Out and Use Reasoning	E22
10 Solids and Shapes	
10-1 Solid Figures	D59
10-2 Relating Solids and Shapes	D59
10-3 Lines and Line Segments	D61
10-4 Angles	D62
10-5 Polygons	D63
10-6 Triangles	D64
10-7 Quadrilaterals	D65
10-8 Make and Test Generalizations	E31
11 Congruence and Symmetry	
11-1 Congruent Figures and Motion	D66
11-2 Line Symmetry	D67
11-3 Drawing Shapes with Lines of Symmetry	D67
11-4 Use Objects	E22
12 Understanding Fractions	
12-1 Dividing Regions into Equal Parts	A42
12-2 Fractions and Regions	A43
12-3 Fractions and Sets	A44
12-4 Benchmark Fractions	A40
12-5 Finding Equivalent Fractions	A48, A49
12-6 Using Models to Compare Fractions	A47
12-7 Fractions on the Number Line	A46, A50
12-8 Using Models to Add Fractions	A52
12-9 Using Models to Subtract Fractions	A53
12-10 Make a Table and Look for a Pattern	E21

Correlation of enVision Math to
Math Diagnosis and Intervention System

Topics and Lessons	Intervention Lesson
13 Decimals and Money	
13-1 Fractions and Decimals	A64
13-2 Using Money to Understand Decimals	A67
13-3 Adding and Subtracting with Money	C35
13-4 Draw a Picture and Write a Number Sentence	E25
13-5 Missing or Extra Information	E5
14 Customary Measurement	
14-1 Understanding Measurement	
14-2 Fractions of an Inch	D37
14-3 Using Inches, Feet, Yards, and Miles	D38
14-4 Customary Units of Capacity	D40
14-5 Units of Weight	D42
14-6 Act It Out and Use Reasoning	E22
15 Metric Measurement	
15-1 Using Centimeters and Decimeters	D39
15-2 Using Meters and Kilometers	D39
15-3 Metric Units of Capacity	D41
15-4 Units of Mass	D43
15-5 Make a Table and Look for a Pattern	E21
16 Perimeter, Area, and Volume	
16-1 Understanding Perimeter	D44
16-2 Perimeter of Common Shapes	D44
16-3 Different Shapes with the Same Perimeter	
16-4 Try, Check, and Revise	E24
16-5 Understanding Area	D45
16-6 Estimating and Measuring Area	D45
16-7 Volume	D46
16-8 Solve a Simpler Problem	E28
17 Time and Temperature	
17-1 Time to the Half Hour and Quarter Hour	D13
17-2 Time to the Minute	D14
17-3 Units of Time	D15
17-4 Elapsed Time	D16
17-5 Temperature	D17
17-6 Work Backward	E30

Correlation of enVision Math to
Math Diagnosis and Intervention System

Topics and Lessons	Intervention Lesson
18 Multiplying Greater Numbers	
18-1 Using Mental Math to Multiply	C41
18-2 Estimating Products	C43
18-3 Multiplication and Arrays	C45
18-4 Breaking Apart to Multiply	C46
18-5 Using an Expanded Algorithm	C46
18-6 Multiplying 2-Digit by 1-Digit Numbers	C47
18-7 Draw a Picture and Write a Number Sentence	E26
19 Dividing with 1-Digit Numbers	
19-1 Mental Math	C42
19-2 Estimating Quotients	C44
19-3 Connecting Models and Symbols	C50
19-4 Dividing 2-Digit numbers	C51
19-5 Dividing with Remainders	C51
19-6 Multiple-Step Problems	E8
20 Data, Graphs, and Probability	
20-1 Organizing Data	D82
20-2 Reading Pictographs and Bar Graphs	D83, D84
20-3 Making Pictographs	D83
20-4 Making Bar Graphs	D84
20-5 Ordered Pairs and Line Graphs	D81
20-6 How Likely?	D86
20-7 Outcomes and Experiments	D87
20-8 Line Plots and Probability	D88
20-9 Use Tables and Graphs to Draw Conclusions	E29